DAILY FOOD LOG AND FOOD TRIGGER TRACKER

FOOD	AMOUNT	TIME	IMMEDIATLY AFTER	1 HOUR	3 HOURS	Proteins	Calories

TOTAL

DATE: _____

WEIGHT

	LOW	MED	HIGH
SLEEP QUALITY	○	○	○
ENERGY LEVEL	○	○	○
ACTIVITY LEVEL	○	○	○

WATER INTAKE

1 CUP = 8 OZ

TODAY'S GOALS

○ _____

○ _____

○ _____

MEDICATIONS/SUPPLEMENTS

_____

_____

_____

_____

_____

_____

EXERCISE

_____

_____

_____

_____

MY MOOD:

NOTES

_____

_____

_____

_____

_____

_____

_____

_____

_____

DAILY FOOD LOG AND FOOD TRIGGER TRACKER

FOOD	AMOUNT	TIME	IMMEDIATLY AFTER	1 HOUR	3 HOURS	Proteins	Calories

TOTAL

DATE: _____

WEIGHT

	LOW	MED	HIGH
SLEEP QUALITY	◯	◯	◯
ENERGY LEVEL	◯	◯	◯
ACTIVITY LEVEL	◯	◯	◯

WATER INTAKE

1 CUP = 8 OZ

TODAY'S GOALS

◯ _____
◯ _____
◯ _____

MEDICATIONS/SUPPLEMENTS

_____
_____
_____
_____
_____
_____

EXERCISE

_____
_____
_____
_____

MY MOOD: 😠 ☹️ 😐 😊 😀 😆 😍

NOTES

_____
_____
_____
_____
_____
_____
_____
_____

DAILY FOOD LOG AND FOOD TRIGGER TRACKER

FOOD	AMOUNT	TIME	IMMEDIATLY AFTER	1 HOUR	3 HOURS	Proteins	Calories

TOTAL

DATE: _____

WEIGHT

	LOW	MED	HIGH
SLEEP QUALITY	○	○	○
ENERGY LEVEL	○	○	○
ACTIVITY LEVEL	○	○	○

WATER INTAKE

1 CUP = 8 OZ

TODAY'S GOALS

○ _____

○ _____

○ _____

MEDICATIONS/SUPPLEMENTS

_____

_____

_____

_____

_____

_____

EXERCISE

_____

_____

_____

_____

MY MOOD:

NOTES

DAILY FOOD LOG AND FOOD TRIGGER TRACKER

FOOD	AMOUNT	TIME	IMMEDIATLY AFTER	1 HOUR	3 HOURS	Proteins	Calories

TOTAL

DATE: _____

	LOW	MED	HIGH
SLEEP QUALITY	◯	◯	◯
ENERGY LEVEL	◯	◯	◯
ACTIVITY LEVEL	◯	◯	◯

WEIGHT

WATER INTAKE

1 CUP = 8 OZ

TODAY'S GOALS

◯ _____
◯ _____
◯ _____

MEDICATIONS/SUPPLEMENTS

_____
_____
_____
_____
_____
_____
_____

EXERCISE

_____
_____
_____
_____

MY MOOD:

NOTES

_____
_____
_____
_____
_____
_____
_____
_____

DAILY FOOD LOG AND FOOD TRIGGER TRACKER

FOOD	AMOUNT	TIME	IMMEDIATLY AFTER	1 HOUR	3 HOURS	Proteins	Calories
							TOTAL

DATE: _____

WEIGHT

	LOW	MED	HIGH
SLEEP QUALITY	○	○	○
ENERGY LEVEL	○	○	○
ACTIVITY LEVEL	○	○	○

WATER INTAKE

1 CUP = 8 OZ

TODAY'S GOALS

○ _____

○ _____

○ _____

MEDICATIONS/SUPPLEMENTS

_____

_____

_____

_____

_____

_____

EXERCISE

_____

_____

_____

_____

MY MOOD:

NOTES

_____

_____

_____

_____

_____

_____

_____

_____

DAILY FOOD LOG AND FOOD TRIGGER TRACKER

FOOD	AMOUNT	TIME	IMMEDIATLY AFTER	1 HOUR	3 HOURS	Proteins	Calories

TOTAL

DATE: _____

WEIGHT

	LOW	MED	HIGH
SLEEP QUALITY	○	○	○
ENERGY LEVEL	○	○	○
ACTIVITY LEVEL	○	○	○

WATER INTAKE

1 CUP = 8 OZ

TODAY'S GOALS

○ _____
○ _____
○ _____

MEDICATIONS/SUPPLEMENTS

_____
_____
_____
_____
_____
_____

EXERCISE

_____
_____
_____
_____

MY MOOD:

NOTES

_____
_____
_____
_____
_____
_____
_____
_____

DAILY FOOD LOG AND FOOD TRIGGER TRACKER

FOOD	AMOUNT	TIME	IMMEDIATLY AFTER	1 HOUR	3 HOURS	Proteins	Calories

TOTAL

WEEKLY MEAL PLANNER

	BREAKFAST	LUNCH	DINNER
MONDAY			
TUESDAY			
WEDNESDAY			
THURSDAY			
FRIDAY			
SATURDAY			
SUNDAY			

DATE: _____

WEIGHT

	LOW	MED	HIGH
SLEEP QUALITY	○	○	○
ENERGY LEVEL	○	○	○
ACTIVITY LEVEL	○	○	○

WATER INTAKE

1 CUP = 8 OZ

TODAY'S GOALS

○ _____
○ _____
○ _____

MEDICATIONS/SUPPLEMENTS

_____
_____
_____
_____
_____
_____

EXERCISE

_____
_____
_____
_____

MY MOOD: 😠 🙁 😐 🙂 😃 😋 😍

NOTES

_____
_____
_____
_____
_____
_____
_____
_____

DAILY FOOD LOG AND FOOD TRIGGER TRACKER

FOOD	AMOUNT	TIME	IMMEDIATLY AFTER	1 HOUR	3 HOURS	Proteins	Calories
							TOTAL

DATE: _____

WEIGHT

	LOW	MED	HIGH
SLEEP QUALITY	○	○	○
ENERGY LEVEL	○	○	○
ACTIVITY LEVEL	○	○	○

WATER INTAKE

1 CUP = 8 OZ

TODAY'S GOALS

○ _____
○ _____
○ _____

MEDICATIONS/SUPPLEMENTS

_____
_____
_____
_____
_____
_____

EXERCISE

_____
_____
_____
_____

MY MOOD:

NOTES

_____
_____
_____
_____
_____
_____
_____
_____

DAILY FOOD LOG AND FOOD TRIGGER TRACKER

FOOD	AMOUNT	TIME	IMMEDIATLY AFTER	1 HOUR	3 HOURS	Proteins	Calories

TOTAL

DATE: _____

WEIGHT

	LOW	MED	HIGH
SLEEP QUALITY	◯	◯	◯
ENERGY LEVEL	◯	◯	◯
ACTIVITY LEVEL	◯	◯	◯

WATER INTAKE

1 CUP = 8 OZ

TODAY'S GOALS

◯ _____
◯ _____
◯ _____

MEDICATIONS/SUPPLEMENTS

_____
_____
_____
_____
_____
_____

EXERCISE

_____
_____
_____
_____

MY MOOD: 😠 🙁 😐 😊 😃 😁 😍

NOTES

_____
_____
_____
_____
_____
_____
_____
_____

DAILY FOOD LOG AND FOOD TRIGGER TRACKER

FOOD	AMOUNT	TIME	IMMEDIATLY AFTER	1 HOUR	3 HOURS	Proteins	Calories

TOTAL

DATE: _____

WEIGHT

		LOW	MED	HIGH
SLEEP QUALITY		◯	◯	◯
ENERGY LEVEL		◯	◯	◯
ACTIVITY LEVEL		◯	◯	◯

WATER INTAKE

1 CUP = 8 OZ

TODAY'S GOALS

◯ _____
◯ _____
◯ _____

MEDICATIONS/SUPPLEMENTS

_____
_____
_____
_____
_____
_____

EXERCISE

_____
_____
_____
_____

MY MOOD: 😠 🙁 😐 🙂 😄 😝 😍

NOTES

_____
_____
_____
_____
_____
_____
_____
_____

DAILY FOOD LOG AND FOOD TRIGGER TRACKER

FOOD	AMOUNT	TIME	IMMEDIATLY AFTER	1 HOUR	3 HOURS	Proteins	Calories

TOTAL

DATE: _____

WEIGHT

	LOW	MED	HIGH
SLEEP QUALITY	○	○	○
ENERGY LEVEL	○	○	○
ACTIVITY LEVEL	○	○	○

WATER INTAKE
1 CUP = 8 OZ

TODAY'S GOALS

○ _____

○ _____

○ _____

MEDICATIONS/SUPPLEMENTS

_____

_____

_____

_____

_____

_____

EXERCISE

_____

_____

_____

_____

MY MOOD:

NOTES

_____

_____

_____

_____

_____

_____

_____

_____

DAILY FOOD LOG AND FOOD TRIGGER TRACKER

FOOD	AMOUNT	TIME	IMMEDIATLY AFTER	1 HOUR	3 HOURS	Proteins	Calories

TOTAL

DATE: _____

WEIGHT

	LOW	MED	HIGH
SLEEP QUALITY	◯	◯	◯
ENERGY LEVEL	◯	◯	◯
ACTIVITY LEVEL	◯	◯	◯

WATER INTAKE

1 CUP = 8 OZ

TODAY'S GOALS

◯ _____

◯ _____

◯ _____

MEDICATIONS/SUPPLEMENTS

_____

_____

_____

_____

_____

_____

EXERCISE

_____

_____

_____

_____

MY MOOD: 😠 🙁 😐 🙂 😄 😁 😍

NOTES

_____

_____

_____

_____

_____

_____

_____

_____

DAILY FOOD LOG AND FOOD TRIGGER TRACKER

FOOD	AMOUNT	TIME	IMMEDIATLY AFTER	1 HOUR	3 HOURS	Proteins	Calories
							TOTAL

DATE: _____

WEIGHT

	LOW	MED	HIGH
SLEEP QUALITY	○	○	○
ENERGY LEVEL	○	○	○
ACTIVITY LEVEL	○	○	○

WATER INTAKE

1 CUP = 8 OZ

TODAY'S GOALS

○ _____
○ _____
○ _____

MEDICATIONS/SUPPLEMENTS

_____
_____
_____
_____
_____
_____

EXERCISE

_____
_____
_____
_____

MY MOOD: 😠 🙁 😐 🙂 😀 😋 😍

NOTES

_____
_____
_____
_____
_____
_____
_____
_____

DAILY FOOD LOG AND FOOD TRIGGER TRACKER

FOOD	AMOUNT	TIME	IMMEDIATLY AFTER	1 HOUR	3 HOURS	Proteins	Calories

TOTAL

WEEKLY MEAL PLANNER

	BREAKFAST	LUNCH	DINNER
MONDAY			
TUESDAY			
WEDNESDAY			
THURSDAY			
FRIDAY			
SATURDAY			
SUNDAY			

DATE: _____

WEIGHT

	LOW	MED	HIGH
SLEEP QUALITY	◯	◯	◯
ENERGY LEVEL	◯	◯	◯
ACTIVITY LEVEL	◯	◯	◯

WATER INTAKE

1 CUP = 8 OZ

TODAY'S GOALS

◯ _____
◯ _____
◯ _____

MEDICATIONS/SUPPLEMENTS

_____
_____
_____
_____
_____
_____
_____

EXERCISE

_____
_____
_____
_____

MY MOOD: 😠 ☹️ 😐 🙂 😄 😋 😍

NOTES

_____
_____
_____
_____
_____
_____
_____
_____

DAILY FOOD LOG AND FOOD TRIGGER TRACKER

FOOD	AMOUNT	TIME	IMMEDIATLY AFTER	1 HOUR	3 HOURS	Proteins	Calories
							TOTAL

DATE: _____

	LOW	MED	HIGH
SLEEP QUALITY	◯	◯	◯
ENERGY LEVEL	◯	◯	◯
ACTIVITY LEVEL	◯	◯	◯

WEIGHT

WATER INTAKE

1 CUP = 8 OZ

TODAY'S GOALS

◯ _____

◯ _____

◯ _____

MEDICATIONS/SUPPLEMENTS

_____

_____

_____

_____

_____

_____

EXERCISE

_____

_____

_____

_____

MY MOOD: 😠 🙁 😐 🙂 😄 😋 😍

NOTES

_____

_____

_____

_____

_____

_____

_____

_____

DAILY FOOD LOG AND FOOD TRIGGER TRACKER

FOOD	AMOUNT	TIME	IMMEDIATLY AFTER	1 HOUR	3 HOURS	Proteins	Calories

TOTAL

DATE: _____

WEIGHT

	LOW	MED	HIGH
SLEEP QUALITY	○	○	○
ENERGY LEVEL	○	○	○
ACTIVITY LEVEL	○	○	○

WATER INTAKE

1 CUP = 8 OZ

TODAY'S GOALS

○ _____
○ _____
○ _____

MEDICATIONS/SUPPLEMENTS

_____
_____
_____
_____
_____
_____

EXERCISE

_____
_____
_____
_____

MY MOOD: 😠 ☹ 😐 🙂 😀 😃 😍

NOTES

_____
_____
_____
_____
_____
_____
_____
_____

DAILY FOOD LOG AND FOOD TRIGGER TRACKER

FOOD	AMOUNT	TIME	IMMEDIATLY AFTER	1 HOUR	3 HOURS	Proteins	Calories
							TOTAL

DATE: _____

WEIGHT

	LOW	MED	HIGH
SLEEP QUALITY	○	○	○
ENERGY LEVEL	○	○	○
ACTIVITY LEVEL	○	○	○

WATER INTAKE

1 CUP = 8 OZ

TODAY'S GOALS

○ _____
○ _____
○ _____

MEDICATIONS/SUPPLEMENTS

_____
_____
_____
_____
_____
_____

EXERCISE

_____
_____
_____
_____

MY MOOD:

NOTES

_____
_____
_____
_____
_____
_____
_____
_____

DAILY FOOD LOG AND FOOD TRIGGER TRACKER

FOOD	AMOUNT	TIME	IMMEDIATLY AFTER	1 HOUR	3 HOURS	Proteins	Calories

TOTAL

DATE: _____

WEIGHT

LOW	MED	HIGH
SLEEP QUALITY	◯	◯	◯
ENERGY LEVEL	◯	◯	◯
ACTIVITY LEVEL	◯	◯	◯

WATER INTAKE

1 CUP = 8 OZ

TODAY'S GOALS

◯ _____
◯ _____
◯ _____

MEDICATIONS/SUPPLEMENTS

_____
_____
_____
_____
_____
_____

EXERCISE

_____
_____
_____
_____

MY MOOD: 😠 🙁 😐 🙂 😃 😁 😍

NOTES

_____
_____
_____
_____
_____
_____
_____
_____

DAILY FOOD LOG AND FOOD TRIGGER TRACKER

FOOD	AMOUNT	TIME	IMMEDIATLY AFTER	1 HOUR	3 HOURS	Proteins	Calories

TOTAL

DATE: _____

	LOW	MED	HIGH
SLEEP QUALITY	◯	◯	◯
ENERGY LEVEL	◯	◯	◯
ACTIVITY LEVEL	◯	◯	◯

WEIGHT

WATER INTAKE

1 CUP = 8 OZ

TODAY'S GOALS

◯ _____

◯ _____

◯ _____

MEDICATIONS/SUPPLEMENTS

_____

_____

_____

_____

_____

_____

EXERCISE

_____

_____

_____

_____

MY MOOD: 😠 🙁 😐 🙂 😄 😁 😍

NOTES

_____

_____

_____

_____

_____

_____

_____

_____

DAILY FOOD LOG AND FOOD TRIGGER TRACKER

FOOD	AMOUNT	TIME	IMMEDIATLY AFTER	1 HOUR	3 HOURS	Proteins	Calories

TOTAL

DATE: _____

WEIGHT

	LOW	MED	HIGH
SLEEP QUALITY	○	○	○
ENERGY LEVEL	○	○	○
ACTIVITY LEVEL	○	○	○

WATER INTAKE

1 CUP = 8 OZ

TODAY'S GOALS

○ _____

○ _____

○ _____

MEDICATIONS/SUPPLEMENTS

_____

_____

_____

_____

_____

_____

EXERCISE

_____

_____

_____

_____

MY MOOD:

NOTES

_____

_____

_____

_____

_____

_____

_____

_____

DAILY FOOD LOG AND FOOD TRIGGER TRACKER

FOOD	AMOUNT	TIME	IMMEDIATLY AFTER	1 HOUR	3 HOURS	Proteins	Calories
							TOTAL

WEEKLY MEAL PLANNER

	BREAKFAST	LUNCH	DINNER
MONDAY			
TUESDAY			
WEDNESDAY			
THURSDAY			
FRIDAY			
SATURDAY			
SUNDAY			

DATE: _____

WEIGHT

	LOW	MED	HIGH
SLEEP QUALITY	◯	◯	◯
ENERGY LEVEL	◯	◯	◯
ACTIVITY LEVEL	◯	◯	◯

WATER INTAKE

1 CUP = 8 OZ

TODAY'S GOALS

◯ _____
◯ _____
◯ _____

MEDICATIONS/SUPPLEMENTS

_____
_____
_____
_____
_____
_____

EXERCISE

_____
_____
_____
_____

MY MOOD: 😠 🙁 😐 🙂 😄 😁 😍

NOTES

_____
_____
_____
_____
_____
_____
_____

DAILY FOOD LOG AND FOOD TRIGGER TRACKER

FOOD	AMOUNT	TIME	IMMEDIATLY AFTER	1 HOUR	3 HOURS	Proteins	Calories

TOTAL

DATE: _____

WEIGHT

	LOW	MED	HIGH
SLEEP QUALITY	○	○	○
ENERGY LEVEL	○	○	○
ACTIVITY LEVEL	○	○	○

WATER INTAKE

1 CUP = 8 OZ

TODAY'S GOALS

○ _____
○ _____
○ _____

MEDICATIONS/SUPPLEMENTS

_____
_____
_____
_____
_____
_____
_____

EXERCISE

_____
_____
_____
_____

MY MOOD: 😠 🙁 😐 😊 😃 😁 😍

NOTES

_____
_____
_____
_____
_____
_____
_____

DAILY FOOD LOG AND FOOD TRIGGER TRACKER

FOOD	AMOUNT	TIME	IMMEDIATLY AFTER	1 HOUR	3 HOURS	Proteins	Calories

TOTAL

DATE: _____

WEIGHT

	LOW	MED	HIGH
SLEEP QUALITY	◯	◯	◯
ENERGY LEVEL	◯	◯	◯
ACTIVITY LEVEL	◯	◯	◯

WATER INTAKE

1 CUP = 8 OZ

TODAY'S GOALS

◯ _____

◯ _____

◯ _____

MEDICATIONS/SUPPLEMENTS

_____

_____

_____

_____

_____

_____

EXERCISE

_____

_____

_____

MY MOOD: 😠 😟 😐 🙂 😃 😋 😍

NOTES

_____

_____

_____

_____

_____

_____

_____

_____

DAILY FOOD LOG AND FOOD TRIGGER TRACKER

FOOD	AMOUNT	TIME	IMMEDIATLY AFTER	1 HOUR	3 HOURS	Proteins	Calories

TOTAL

DATE: _____

WEIGHT

	LOW	MED	HIGH
SLEEP QUALITY	○	○	○
ENERGY LEVEL	○	○	○
ACTIVITY LEVEL	○	○	○

WATER INTAKE

1 CUP = 8 OZ

TODAY'S GOALS

○ _____
○ _____
○ _____

MEDICATIONS/SUPPLEMENTS

_____
_____
_____
_____
_____
_____
_____

EXERCISE

_____
_____
_____

MY MOOD:

NOTES

_____
_____
_____
_____
_____
_____
_____
_____

DAILY FOOD LOG AND FOOD TRIGGER TRACKER

FOOD	AMOUNT	TIME	IMMEDIATLY AFTER	1 HOUR	3 HOURS	Proteins	Calories
							TOTAL

DATE: _____

WEIGHT

			LOW	MED	HIGH
SLEEP QUALITY			○	○	○
ENERGY LEVEL			○	○	○
ACTIVITY LEVEL			○	○	○

WATER INTAKE
1 CUP = 8 OZ

TODAY'S GOALS
○ _____
○ _____
○ _____

MEDICATIONS/SUPPLEMENTS
_____
_____
_____
_____
_____
_____

EXERCISE
_____
_____
_____
_____

MY MOOD:

NOTES
_____
_____
_____
_____
_____
_____
_____

DAILY FOOD LOG AND FOOD TRIGGER TRACKER

FOOD	AMOUNT	TIME	IMMEDIATLY AFTER	1 HOUR	3 HOURS	Proteins	Calories

TOTAL

DATE: _____

WEIGHT

	LOW	MED	HIGH
SLEEP QUALITY	○	○	○
ENERGY LEVEL	○	○	○
ACTIVITY LEVEL	○	○	○

WATER INTAKE

1 CUP = 8 OZ

TODAY'S GOALS

○ _____

○ _____

○ _____

MEDICATIONS/SUPPLEMENTS

_____

_____

_____

_____

_____

_____

EXERCISE

_____

_____

_____

_____

MY MOOD:

NOTES

_____

_____

_____

_____

_____

_____

_____

_____

DAILY FOOD LOG AND FOOD TRIGGER TRACKER

FOOD	AMOUNT	TIME	IMMEDIATLY AFTER	1 HOUR	3 HOURS	Proteins	Calories
							TOTAL

DATE: _____

WEIGHT

	LOW	MED	HIGH
SLEEP QUALITY	○	○	○
ENERGY LEVEL	○	○	○
ACTIVITY LEVEL	○	○	○

WATER INTAKE

1 CUP = 8 OZ

TODAY'S GOALS

○ _____
○ _____
○ _____

MEDICATIONS/SUPPLEMENTS

_____
_____
_____
_____
_____
_____

EXERCISE

_____
_____
_____
_____

MY MOOD: 😠 🙁 😐 😊 😀 😁 😍

NOTES

_____
_____
_____
_____
_____
_____
_____
_____

DAILY FOOD LOG AND FOOD TRIGGER TRACKER

FOOD	AMOUNT	TIME	IMMEDIATLY AFTER	1 HOUR	3 HOURS	Proteins	Calories

TOTAL

WEEKLY MEAL PLANNER

	BREAKFAST	LUNCH	DINNER
MONDAY			
TUESDAY			
WEDNESDAY			
THURSDAY			
FRIDAY			
SATURDAY			
SUNDAY			

DATE: _____

WEIGHT

	LOW	MED	HIGH
SLEEP QUALITY	◯	◯	◯
ENERGY LEVEL	◯	◯	◯
ACTIVITY LEVEL	◯	◯	◯

WATER INTAKE

1 CUP = 8 OZ

TODAY'S GOALS

◯ _____
◯ _____
◯ _____

MEDICATIONS/SUPPLEMENTS

_____
_____
_____
_____
_____
_____
_____

EXERCISE

_____
_____
_____
_____

MY MOOD: 😠 🙁 😐 😊 😃 😁 😍

NOTES

_____
_____
_____
_____
_____
_____
_____
_____

DAILY FOOD LOG AND FOOD TRIGGER TRACKER

FOOD	AMOUNT	TIME	IMMEDIATLY AFTER	1 HOUR	3 HOURS	Proteins	Calories
							TOTAL

DATE: _____

WEIGHT

	LOW	MED	HIGH
SLEEP QUALITY	◯	◯	◯
ENERGY LEVEL	◯	◯	◯
ACTIVITY LEVEL	◯	◯	◯

WATER INTAKE

1 CUP = 8 OZ

TODAY'S GOALS

◯ _____

◯ _____

◯ _____

MEDICATIONS/SUPPLEMENTS

_____

_____

_____

_____

_____

_____

EXERCISE

_____

_____

_____

_____

MY MOOD:

NOTES

_____

_____

_____

_____

_____

_____

_____

_____

DAILY FOOD LOG AND FOOD TRIGGER TRACKER

FOOD	AMOUNT	TIME	IMMEDIATLY AFTER	1 HOUR	3 HOURS	Proteins	Calories

TOTAL

DATE: _____

WEIGHT

	LOW	MED	HIGH
SLEEP QUALITY	○	○	○
ENERGY LEVEL	○	○	○
ACTIVITY LEVEL	○	○	○

WATER INTAKE

1 CUP = 8 OZ

TODAY'S GOALS

○ _____
○ _____
○ _____

MEDICATIONS/SUPPLEMENTS

_____
_____
_____
_____
_____
_____

EXERCISE

_____
_____
_____
_____

MY MOOD:

NOTES

_____
_____
_____
_____
_____
_____
_____
_____

DAILY FOOD LOG AND FOOD TRIGGER TRACKER

FOOD	AMOUNT	TIME	IMMEDIATLY AFTER	1 HOUR	3 HOURS	Proteins	Calories

TOTAL

DATE: _____

WEIGHT

	LOW	MED	HIGH
SLEEP QUALITY	○	○	○
ENERGY LEVEL	○	○	○
ACTIVITY LEVEL	○	○	○

WATER INTAKE

1 CUP = 8 OZ

TODAY'S GOALS

○ _____
○ _____
○ _____

MEDICATIONS/SUPPLEMENTS

_____
_____
_____
_____
_____
_____

EXERCISE

_____
_____
_____
_____

MY MOOD:

NOTES

_____
_____
_____
_____
_____
_____
_____
_____

DAILY FOOD LOG AND FOOD TRIGGER TRACKER

FOOD	AMOUNT	TIME	IMMEDIATLY AFTER	1 HOUR	3 HOURS	Proteins	Calories

TOTAL

DATE: _____

WEIGHT

LOW	MED	HIGH
SLEEP QUALITY	○	○	○
ENERGY LEVEL	○	○	○
ACTIVITY LEVEL	○	○	○

WATER INTAKE

1 CUP = 8 OZ

TODAY'S GOALS

○ _____
○ _____
○ _____

MEDICATIONS/SUPPLEMENTS

_____
_____
_____
_____
_____
_____
_____

EXERCISE

_____
_____
_____
_____

MY MOOD:

NOTES

_____
_____
_____
_____
_____
_____
_____
_____

DAILY FOOD LOG AND FOOD TRIGGER TRACKER

FOOD	AMOUNT	TIME	IMMEDIATLY AFTER	1 HOUR	3 HOURS	Proteins	Calories

TOTAL

DATE: _____

WEIGHT

		LOW	MED	HIGH
SLEEP QUALITY		◯	◯	◯
ENERGY LEVEL		◯	◯	◯
ACTIVITY LEVEL		◯	◯	◯

WATER INTAKE

1 CUP = 8 OZ

TODAY'S GOALS

◯ _____
◯ _____
◯ _____

MEDICATIONS/SUPPLEMENTS

_____
_____
_____
_____
_____
_____

EXERCISE

_____
_____
_____
_____

MY MOOD:

NOTES

_____
_____
_____
_____
_____
_____
_____
_____

DAILY FOOD LOG AND FOOD TRIGGER TRACKER

FOOD	AMOUNT	TIME	IMMEDIATLY AFTER	1 HOUR	3 HOURS	Proteins	Calories

TOTAL

DATE: _____

WEIGHT

	LOW	MED	HIGH
SLEEP QUALITY	○	○	○
ENERGY LEVEL	○	○	○
ACTIVITY LEVEL	○	○	○

WATER INTAKE

1 CUP = 8 OZ

TODAY'S GOALS

○ _____
○ _____
○ _____

MEDICATIONS/SUPPLEMENTS

_____
_____
_____
_____
_____
_____

EXERCISE

_____
_____
_____
_____

MY MOOD:

NOTES

_____
_____
_____
_____
_____
_____
_____

DAILY FOOD LOG AND FOOD TRIGGER TRACKER

FOOD	AMOUNT	TIME	IMMEDIATLY AFTER	1 HOUR	3 HOURS	Proteins	Calories

TOTAL

WEEKLY MEAL PLANNER

	BREAKFAST	LUNCH	DINNER
MONDAY			
TUESDAY			
WEDNESDAY			
THURSDAY			
FRIDAY			
SATURDAY			
SUNDAY			

DATE: _____

WEIGHT

	LOW	MED	HIGH
SLEEP QUALITY	○	○	○
ENERGY LEVEL	○	○	○
ACTIVITY LEVEL	○	○	○

WATER INTAKE

1 CUP = 8 OZ

TODAY'S GOALS

○ _____
○ _____
○ _____

MEDICATIONS/SUPPLEMENTS

_____
_____
_____
_____
_____
_____
_____

EXERCISE

_____
_____
_____
_____

MY MOOD:

NOTES

_____
_____
_____
_____
_____
_____
_____
_____

DAILY FOOD LOG AND FOOD TRIGGER TRACKER

FOOD	AMOUNT	TIME	IMMEDIATLY AFTER	1 HOUR	3 HOURS	Proteins	Calories

TOTAL

DATE: _____

WEIGHT

	LOW	MED	HIGH
SLEEP QUALITY	◯	◯	◯
ENERGY LEVEL	◯	◯	◯
ACTIVITY LEVEL	◯	◯	◯

WATER INTAKE

1 CUP = 8 OZ

TODAY'S GOALS

◯ _____
◯ _____
◯ _____

MEDICATIONS/SUPPLEMENTS

_____
_____
_____
_____
_____
_____

EXERCISE

_____
_____
_____
_____

MY MOOD:

NOTES

_____
_____
_____
_____
_____
_____
_____
_____

DAILY FOOD LOG AND FOOD TRIGGER TRACKER

FOOD	AMOUNT	TIME	IMMEDIATLY AFTER	1 HOUR	3 HOURS	Proteins	Calories

TOTAL

DATE: _____

WEIGHT

	LOW	MED	HIGH
SLEEP QUALITY	◯	◯	◯
ENERGY LEVEL	◯	◯	◯
ACTIVITY LEVEL	◯	◯	◯

WATER INTAKE

1 CUP = 8 OZ

TODAY'S GOALS

◯ _____
◯ _____
◯ _____

MEDICATIONS/SUPPLEMENTS

_____
_____
_____
_____
_____
_____

EXERCISE

_____
_____
_____
_____

MY MOOD: 😠 ☹️ 😐 🙂 😀 😆 😍

NOTES

_____
_____
_____
_____
_____
_____
_____
_____

DAILY FOOD LOG AND FOOD TRIGGER TRACKER

FOOD	AMOUNT	TIME	IMMEDIATLY AFTER	1 HOUR	3 HOURS	Proteins	Calories

TOTAL

DATE: _____

WEIGHT

	LOW	MED	HIGH
SLEEP QUALITY	○	○	○
ENERGY LEVEL	○	○	○
ACTIVITY LEVEL	○	○	○

WATER INTAKE

1 CUP = 8 OZ

TODAY'S GOALS

○ _____
○ _____
○ _____

MEDICATIONS/SUPPLEMENTS

_____
_____
_____
_____
_____
_____

EXERCISE

_____
_____
_____
_____

MY MOOD:

NOTES

_____
_____
_____
_____
_____
_____
_____
_____

DAILY FOOD LOG AND FOOD TRIGGER TRACKER

FOOD	AMOUNT	TIME	IMMEDIATLY AFTER	1 HOUR	3 HOURS	Proteins	Calories

TOTAL

DATE: _____

	LOW	MED	HIGH
SLEEP QUALITY	◯	◯	◯
ENERGY LEVEL	◯	◯	◯
ACTIVITY LEVEL	◯	◯	◯

WEIGHT

WATER INTAKE

1 CUP = 8 OZ

TODAY'S GOALS

◯ _____

◯ _____

◯ _____

MEDICATIONS/SUPPLEMENTS

_____

_____

_____

_____

_____

_____

EXERCISE

_____

_____

_____

_____

MY MOOD: 😠 ☹️ 😐 😊 😃 😁 😍

NOTES

_____

_____

_____

_____

_____

_____

_____

_____

DAILY FOOD LOG AND FOOD TRIGGER TRACKER

FOOD	AMOUNT	TIME	IMMEDIATLY AFTER	1 HOUR	3 HOURS	Proteins	Calories

TOTAL

DATE: _____

WEIGHT

WATER INTAKE

1 CUP = 8 OZ

	LOW	MED	HIGH
SLEEP QUALITY	○	○	○
ENERGY LEVEL	○	○	○
ACTIVITY LEVEL	○	○	○

TODAY'S GOALS

○ _____
○ _____
○ _____

MEDICATIONS/SUPPLEMENTS

_____
_____
_____
_____
_____
_____

EXERCISE

_____
_____
_____
_____

MY MOOD:

NOTES

_____
_____
_____
_____
_____
_____
_____
_____

DAILY FOOD LOG AND FOOD TRIGGER TRACKER

FOOD	AMOUNT	TIME	IMMEDIATLY AFTER	1 HOUR	3 HOURS	Proteins	Calories

TOTAL

DATE: _____

WEIGHT

	LOW	MED	HIGH
SLEEP QUALITY	○	○	○
ENERGY LEVEL	○	○	○
ACTIVITY LEVEL	○	○	○

WATER INTAKE

1 CUP = 8 OZ

TODAY'S GOALS

○ _____
○ _____
○ _____

MEDICATIONS/SUPPLEMENTS

_____
_____
_____
_____
_____
_____

EXERCISE

_____
_____
_____
_____

MY MOOD:

NOTES

_____
_____
_____
_____
_____
_____
_____
_____

DAILY FOOD LOG AND FOOD TRIGGER TRACKER

FOOD	AMOUNT	TIME	IMMEDIATLY AFTER	1 HOUR	3 HOURS	Proteins	Calories

TOTAL

WEEKLY MEAL PLANNER

	BREAKFAST	LUNCH	DINNER
MONDAY			
TUESDAY			
WEDNESDAY			
THURSDAY			
FRIDAY			
SATURDAY			
SUNDAY			

DATE: _____

WEIGHT

WATER INTAKE

1 CUP = 8 OZ

	LOW	MED	HIGH
SLEEP QUALITY	○	○	○
ENERGY LEVEL	○	○	○
ACTIVITY LEVEL	○	○	○

TODAY'S GOALS

○ _____
○ _____
○ _____

MEDICATIONS/SUPPLEMENTS

_____
_____
_____
_____
_____
_____

EXERCISE

_____
_____
_____
_____

MY MOOD:

NOTES

_____
_____
_____
_____
_____
_____
_____
_____

DAILY FOOD LOG AND FOOD TRIGGER TRACKER

FOOD	AMOUNT	TIME	IMMEDIATLY AFTER	1 HOUR	3 HOURS	Proteins	Calories

TOTAL

DATE: _____

WEIGHT

	LOW	MED	HIGH
SLEEP QUALITY	○	○	○
ENERGY LEVEL	○	○	○
ACTIVITY LEVEL	○	○	○

WATER INTAKE

1 CUP = 8 OZ

TODAY'S GOALS

○ _____

○ _____

○ _____

EXERCISE

_____

_____

_____

_____

MEDICATIONS/SUPPLEMENTS

_____

_____

_____

_____

_____

_____

MY MOOD:

NOTES

_____

_____

_____

_____

_____

_____

_____

DAILY FOOD LOG AND FOOD TRIGGER TRACKER

FOOD	AMOUNT	TIME	IMMEDIATLY AFTER	1 HOUR	3 HOURS	Proteins	Calories

TOTAL

DATE: _____

WEIGHT

	LOW	MED	HIGH
SLEEP QUALITY	◯	◯	◯
ENERGY LEVEL	◯	◯	◯
ACTIVITY LEVEL	◯	◯	◯

WATER INTAKE

1 CUP = 8 OZ

TODAY'S GOALS

◯ _____

◯ _____

◯ _____

MEDICATIONS/SUPPLEMENTS

_____

_____

_____

_____

_____

_____

EXERCISE

_____

_____

_____

_____

MY MOOD:

NOTES

_____

_____

_____

_____

_____

_____

_____

_____

DAILY FOOD LOG AND FOOD TRIGGER TRACKER

FOOD	AMOUNT	TIME	IMMEDIATLY AFTER	1 HOUR	3 HOURS	Proteins	Calories

TOTAL

DATE: _____

WEIGHT

	LOW	MED	HIGH
SLEEP QUALITY	○	○	○
ENERGY LEVEL	○	○	○
ACTIVITY LEVEL	○	○	○

WATER INTAKE

1 CUP = 8 OZ

TODAY'S GOALS

○ _____
○ _____
○ _____

MEDICATIONS/SUPPLEMENTS

_____
_____
_____
_____
_____
_____

EXERCISE

_____
_____
_____
_____

MY MOOD:

NOTES

_____
_____
_____
_____
_____
_____
_____
_____

DAILY FOOD LOG AND FOOD TRIGGER TRACKER

FOOD	AMOUNT	TIME	IMMEDIATLY AFTER	1 HOUR	3 HOURS	Proteins	Calories

TOTAL

DATE: _____

WEIGHT

	LOW	MED	HIGH
SLEEP QUALITY	○	○	○
ENERGY LEVEL	○	○	○
ACTIVITY LEVEL	○	○	○

WATER INTAKE

1 CUP = 8 OZ

TODAY'S GOALS

○ _____

○ _____

○ _____

MEDICATIONS/SUPPLEMENTS

_____

_____

_____

_____

_____

_____

EXERCISE

_____

_____

_____

_____

MY MOOD:

NOTES

_____

_____

_____

_____

_____

_____

_____

_____

DAILY FOOD LOG AND FOOD TRIGGER TRACKER

FOOD	AMOUNT	TIME	IMMEDIATLY AFTER	1 HOUR	3 HOURS	Proteins	Calories

TOTAL

DATE: _____

WEIGHT

	LOW	MED	HIGH
SLEEP QUALITY	○	○	○
ENERGY LEVEL	○	○	○
ACTIVITY LEVEL	○	○	○

WATER INTAKE

1 CUP = 8 OZ

TODAY'S GOALS

○ _____
○ _____
○ _____

MEDICATIONS/SUPPLEMENTS

_____
_____
_____
_____
_____
_____

EXERCISE

_____
_____
_____
_____

MY MOOD: 😠 ☹️ 😐 🙂 😃 😁 😍

NOTES

_____
_____
_____
_____
_____
_____
_____
_____

DAILY FOOD LOG AND FOOD TRIGGER TRACKER

FOOD	AMOUNT	TIME	IMMEDIATLY AFTER	1 HOUR	3 HOURS	Proteins	Calories

TOTAL

DATE: _____

WEIGHT

	LOW	MED	HIGH
SLEEP QUALITY	○	○	○
ENERGY LEVEL	○	○	○
ACTIVITY LEVEL	○	○	○

WATER INTAKE
1 CUP = 8 OZ

TODAY'S GOALS

○ _____
○ _____
○ _____

MEDICATIONS/SUPPLEMENTS

_____
_____
_____
_____
_____
_____

EXERCISE

_____
_____
_____
_____

MY MOOD: ☹ ☹ 😐 🙂 😀 😁 😍

NOTES

_____
_____
_____
_____
_____
_____
_____
_____

DAILY FOOD LOG AND FOOD TRIGGER TRACKER

FOOD	AMOUNT	TIME	IMMEDIATLY AFTER	1 HOUR	3 HOURS	Proteins	Calories

TOTAL

WEEKLY MEAL PLANNER

	BREAKFAST	LUNCH	DINNER
MONDAY			
TUESDAY			
WEDNESDAY			
THURSDAY			
FRIDAY			
SATURDAY			
SUNDAY			

DATE: _____

WEIGHT

	LOW	MED	HIGH
SLEEP QUALITY	◯	◯	◯
ENERGY LEVEL	◯	◯	◯
ACTIVITY LEVEL	◯	◯	◯

WATER INTAKE

1 CUP = 8 OZ

TODAY'S GOALS

◯ _____
◯ _____
◯ _____

MEDICATIONS/SUPPLEMENTS

_____
_____
_____
_____
_____
_____

EXERCISE

_____
_____
_____
_____

MY MOOD: 😠 🙁 😐 😌 😀 😬 😍

NOTES

_____
_____
_____
_____
_____
_____
_____
_____

DAILY FOOD LOG AND FOOD TRIGGER TRACKER

FOOD	AMOUNT	TIME	IMMEDIATLY AFTER	1 HOUR	3 HOURS	Proteins	Calories

TOTAL

DATE: _____

WEIGHT

		LOW	MED	HIGH
SLEEP QUALITY		○	○	○
ENERGY LEVEL		○	○	○
ACTIVITY LEVEL		○	○	○

WATER INTAKE

1 CUP = 8 OZ

TODAY'S GOALS

○ _____

○ _____

○ _____

MEDICATIONS/SUPPLEMENTS

_____

_____

_____

_____

_____

_____

EXERCISE

_____

_____

_____

MY MOOD:

NOTES

_____

_____

_____

_____

_____

_____

_____

_____

DAILY FOOD LOG AND FOOD TRIGGER TRACKER

FOOD	AMOUNT	TIME	IMMEDIATELY AFTER	1 HOUR	3 HOURS	Proteins	Calories

TOTAL

DATE: _____

WEIGHT

	LOW	MED	HIGH
SLEEP QUALITY	○	○	○
ENERGY LEVEL	○	○	○
ACTIVITY LEVEL	○	○	○

WATER INTAKE

1 CUP = 8 OZ

TODAY'S GOALS

○ _____
○ _____
○ _____

MEDICATIONS/SUPPLEMENTS

_____
_____
_____
_____
_____
_____
_____

EXERCISE

_____
_____
_____
_____

MY MOOD: 😠 🙁 😐 😌 😀 😃 😍

NOTES

_____
_____
_____
_____
_____
_____
_____
_____

DAILY FOOD LOG AND FOOD TRIGGER TRACKER

FOOD	AMOUNT	TIME	IMMEDIATLY AFTER	1 HOUR	3 HOURS	Proteins	Calories

TOTAL

DATE: _____

WEIGHT

	LOW	MED	HIGH
SLEEP QUALITY	○	○	○
ENERGY LEVEL	○	○	○
ACTIVITY LEVEL	○	○	○

WATER INTAKE

1 CUP = 8 OZ

TODAY'S GOALS

○ _____
○ _____
○ _____

MEDICATIONS/SUPPLEMENTS

_____
_____
_____
_____
_____
_____

EXERCISE

_____
_____
_____
_____

MY MOOD:

NOTES

_____
_____
_____
_____
_____
_____
_____
_____

DAILY FOOD LOG AND FOOD TRIGGER TRACKER

FOOD	AMOUNT	TIME	IMMEDIATLY AFTER	1 HOUR	3 HOURS	Proteins	Calories

TOTAL

DATE: _____

WEIGHT

	LOW	MED	HIGH
SLEEP QUALITY	○	○	○
ENERGY LEVEL	○	○	○
ACTIVITY LEVEL	○	○	○

WATER INTAKE

1 CUP = 8 OZ

TODAY'S GOALS

○ _____

○ _____

○ _____

MEDICATIONS/SUPPLEMENTS

_____

_____

_____

_____

_____

_____

EXERCISE

_____

_____

_____

_____

MY MOOD:

NOTES

_____

_____

_____

_____

_____

_____

_____

_____

DAILY FOOD LOG AND FOOD TRIGGER TRACKER

FOOD	AMOUNT	TIME	IMMEDIATLY AFTER	1 HOUR	3 HOURS	Proteins	Calories

TOTAL

DATE: _____

WEIGHT

	LOW	MED	HIGH
SLEEP QUALITY	○	○	○
ENERGY LEVEL	○	○	○
ACTIVITY LEVEL	○	○	○

WATER INTAKE

1 CUP = 8 OZ

TODAY'S GOALS

○ _____
○ _____
○ _____

MEDICATIONS/SUPPLEMENTS

_____
_____
_____
_____
_____
_____

EXERCISE

_____
_____
_____
_____

MY MOOD: 😠 ☹️ 😐 🙂 😀 😄 😍

NOTES

_____
_____
_____
_____
_____
_____
_____
_____

DAILY FOOD LOG AND FOOD TRIGGER TRACKER

FOOD	AMOUNT	TIME	IMMEDIATLY AFTER	1 HOUR	3 HOURS	Proteins	Calories

TOTAL

DATE: _____

WEIGHT

	LOW	MED	HIGH
SLEEP QUALITY	◯	◯	◯
ENERGY LEVEL	◯	◯	◯
ACTIVITY LEVEL	◯	◯	◯

WATER INTAKE

1 CUP = 8 OZ

TODAY'S GOALS

◯ _____
◯ _____
◯ _____

MEDICATIONS/SUPPLEMENTS

_____
_____
_____
_____
_____
_____

EXERCISE

_____
_____
_____
_____

MY MOOD: 😠 🙁 😐 🙂 😃 😁 😍

NOTES

_____
_____
_____
_____
_____
_____
_____
_____

DAILY FOOD LOG AND FOOD TRIGGER TRACKER

FOOD	AMOUNT	TIME	IMMEDIATLY AFTER	1 HOUR	3 HOURS	Proteins	Calories

TOTAL

WEEKLY MEAL PLANNER

	BREAKFAST	LUNCH	DINNER
MONDAY			
TUESDAY			
WEDNESDAY			
THURSDAY			
FRIDAY			
SATURDAY			
SUNDAY			

Made in the USA
Coppell, TX
26 October 2021